POPULAR LECTURES IN MATHEMATICS SERIES

Editors: I. N. Sneddon and M. Stark

Volume 3

SOME APPLICATIONS OF MECHANICS TO MATHEMATICS

TITLES IN THE POPULAR LECTURES IN MATHEMATICS SERIES

Vol. 1 *The Method of Mathematical Induction*
By I. S. SOMINSKII

Vol. 2 *Fibonacci Numbers*
By N. N. VOROB'EV

Vol. 3 *Some Applications of Mechanics to Mathematics*
By V. A. USPENSKII

Vol. 4 *Geometrical Constructions using Compasses Only*
By A. N. KOSTOVSKII

Vol. 5 *The Ruler in Geometrical Constructions*
By A. S. SMOGORZHEVSKII

Vol. 6 *Inequalities*
By P. P. KOROVKIN

SOME APPLICATIONS OF MECHANICS TO MATHEMATICS

by
V. A. USPENSKII

Translated from the Russian by
HALINA MOSS, B.Sc.

Translation Editor
IAN N. SNEDDON
Simson Professor of Mathematics
in the University of Glasgow

BLAISDELL PUBLISHING COMPANY

NEW YORK · LONDON

A DIVISION OF RANDOM HOUSE

SOLE DISTRIBUTORS IN THE UNITED STATES AND CANADA
Blaisdell Publishing Company
22 East 51st Street, New York 22, N.Y.

Copyright © 1961
PERGAMON PRESS LTD.

A translation of the original volume
Nekotoryye prilozheniya mekhaniki k matematike
(Moscow, Fizmatgiz, 1958)

Library of Congress Card Number: 61-11535

Printed in Great Britain by Pergamon Printing and Art Services Limited, London

CONTENTS

		Page
Foreword		vii
1.	Problem on a tangent to a circle	1
2.	Problem on a tangent to an ellipse	5
3.	Problems on tangents to parabolas and hyperbolas	11
4.	Principle of least potential energy	18
5.	Material points and the centre of gravity	23
6.	The centre of gravity and a system of two material points	28
7.	Theorems about the intersection of straight lines	30
8.	The centre of gravity of a rod with many loads	35
9.	A problem in the theory of numbers (formulation)	39
10.	A problem in the theory of numbers (solution)	43
11.	The impossibility of perpetual motion	49
Conclusion		51

FOREWORD

The applications of mathematics to physics (in particular, to mechanics) are well-known. We need only open a school text-book to find examples. The higher branches of mechanics demand a complex and refined mathematical apparatus.

There are, however, mathematical problems for whose solution we can successfully use the ideas and laws of physics. A number of problems of this kind soluble by methods drawn from mechanics (namely, by using the laws of equilibrium) were given by the author in his lecture "The solving of mathematical problems by the methods of mechanics", which was read to pupils in their seventh year of secondary school at the Moscow State University on 19 February 1956; this lecture, with very minor additions, makes up the contents of this article.

The author is deeply grateful to Isaak Moiseyevich Yaglom, whose detailed remarks helped to reduce the number of deficiencies in this book.

1. PROBLEM ON A TANGENT TO A CIRCLE

As is well-known, a tangent to a circle is the name of a straight line which has exactly one point in common with the circle (the point is called the point of contact). In geometry text-books there is a proof that the tangent is perpendicular to the radius joining the centre of the circle and the point of contact.

We shall demonstrate a proof of this theorem based on mechanical considerations. To do so let us carry out the following experiment mentally. Let us imagine that a small weight hangs at the end M of a thread. The other end of the thread is fastened to the point O.

From everyday experience the reader knows, of course, that in this situation:

(A) <u>The weight is situated at the lowest of all possible positions it could occupy while tied to a thread.</u>

This fact, which has a decisive significance in our reasoning, is completely obvious by itself; it is useful, however, to note that it represents a particular case of a certain general regularity (formulated in the so-called "principle of minimum potential energy") which we shall encounter in more complex circumstances in Section 4. More exactly, with the help of the above-mentioned principle of minimum potential energy, the statement (A) can be deduced from the following self-evident statement (E).

(E) <u>There exists only one position of equilibrium of the weight, i.e. the position of the weight at rest is fully determined by the position of the point O and by the length of the thread.</u>

From the uniqueness of the position of equilibrium (statement E) it follows further that

(C) <u>The weight is situated on the vertical straight line</u>

2 SOME APPLICATIONS OF MECHANICS TO MATHEMATICS

drawn through the point of suspension.

Indeed, if the weight were not situated on this vertical straight line we could obtain a new position of equilibrium by rotating the thread with the weight about that vertical line (Fig. 1).

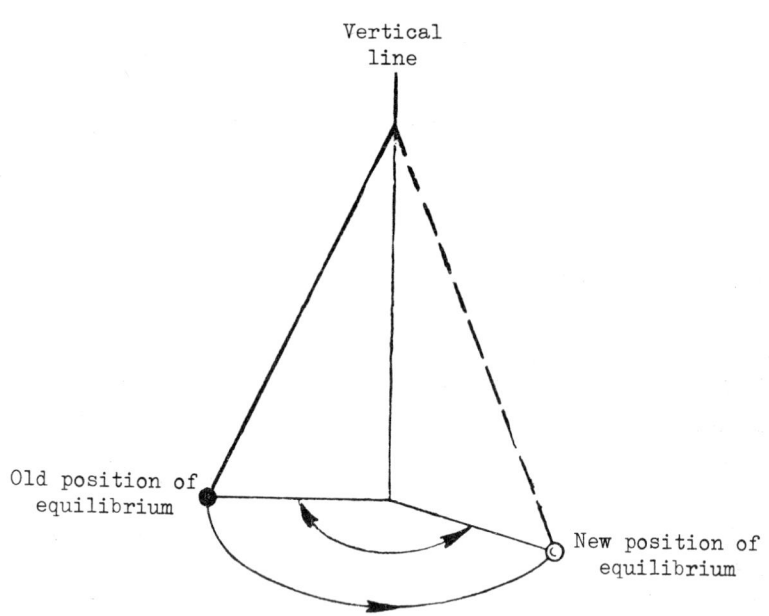

Fig. 1

In this reasoning we thus use as a basis one more fact known from experience:

(S) If a body or a system of bodies which is in a position of equilibrium is rotated about a vertical straight line its new position is also a position of equilibrium.

It follows from statements (A) and (C), that

(B) <u>The distance from the weight to the point of suspension O equals the length of the thread MO (this means that the thread is taut</u>).

We note in passing that the statements (B) and (C) are, of course, no less self-evident than the ones from which they were deduced.

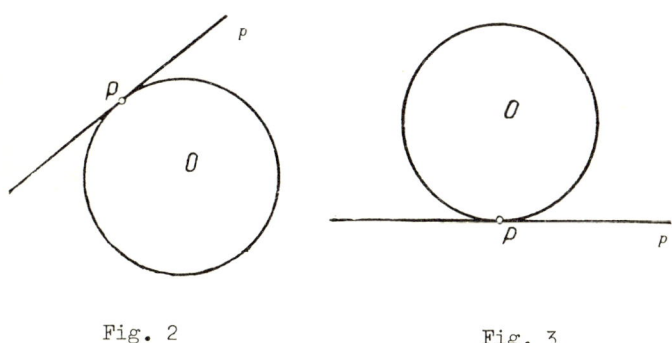

Fig. 2   Fig. 3

We now pass on to proving our theorem. Let us (Fig. 2) be given a circle, centre O, and a straight line p touching this circle at the point P. It is required to prove that OP is perpendicular to p. We resketch our figure on a vertical wall in such a way that the straight line p is horizontal and the circle is situated above the straight line p. (If we stand this book vertically on its lower edge, Fig. 3 will satisy the above requirements.) We note that the point P will be, in this case, the lowest point on the circle. Now, let us take a thread whose length equals the radius of the circle, and let us fasten one end of it at the centre O of the circle. At the other end, which we denote by the letter M, we attach a weight and we suspend it by the thread. We shall show that the end M will arrive at the point P. Indeed, firstly, in accordance with (B), the end M can be situated only on the circle; secondly, in accordance with (A), this end is situated at the lowest point of this circle, i.e. at P. Thus, the thread lies along the radius OP. Therefore, this radius is perpendicular to the straight line p, in accordance with (C), which is the required result.

The example just analysed is, of course, not very interesting, since it is devoted to proving a well-known and fairly simple theorem. However, this very method will be applied later to proving new theorems. In doing so, we shall find the habits acquired in this section in the process of the "mechanical" proof of the theorem on a tangent to a circle very useful. In the next section, we shall first of all tackle a natural generalization of this theorem, namely, the theorem about a tangent to an ellipse.

2. PROBLEM ON A TANGENT TO AN ELLIPSE

A circle is defined as the locus of points A whose distance AO from the fixed point O equals a fixed number l. A more general form of this definition is the definition of the ellipse. The locus of points A, the sum of whose distances $AO_1 + AO_2$ from two fixed points O_1 and O_2 is equal to a fixed number l, is called an <u>ellipse</u> (Fig. 4). The points O_1 and O_2 are called the <u>foci</u> of the ellipse and l is the length of the <u>major axis</u> of the ellipse. The segments AO_1 and AO_2 connecting any point A on the ellipse and the foci are called <u>focal radii</u>, drawn to the point A. A circle is a particular case of an ellipse, when the points O_1 and O_2 coincide. The focal radii in this case also coincide and are equal to the radius of the circle.

Anyone can draw an ellipse if he or she takes a thread, fastens both ends at some points O_1 and O_2 chosen on a sheet of paper so that the distance O_1O_2 is less than the length of the thread, and then draws a curve by stretching the thread with the point of the pencil (Fig. 5).

Just as in the case of the circle, a straight line is called a tangent to the ellipse if it has exactly one point in common with it (Fig. 6).

We have the following theorem about a tangent to an ellipse: <u>the tangent to an ellipse makes equal angles with the focal radii at the point of contact</u>. (In Fig. 6 such equal angles are the angles KPO_1 and LPO_2).

A particular case of this theorem is the theorem about a tangent to a circle. Indeed, in the case of a circle both focal radii coincide; the theorem about a tangent to an ellipse, therefore, takes the following form in the case of a circle: a tangent forms equal complementary angles with the radius drawn at the point of contact; and this signifies the perpendicularity of tangent and radius.

We shall now give a proof of the theorem on a tangent to

an ellipse, similar to the one we gave for the theorem on a tangent to a circle. We suggest that the reader attempts to invent his own "mechanical" proof before he reads on.

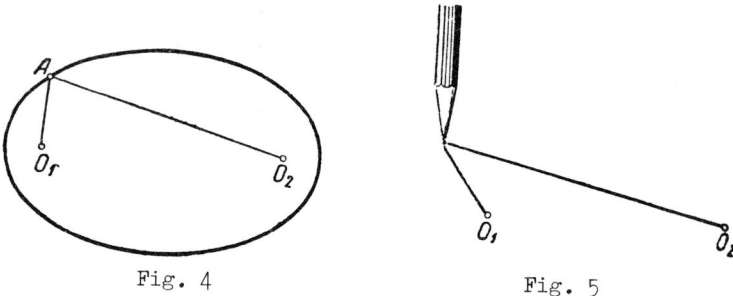

Fig. 4   Fig. 5

Just as in the preceding section, we shall carry out a certain mechanical experiment before giving the proof.

In a vertical plane, we fix two points $\bar{O}_1$ and $\bar{O}_2$ both at the same height. We then take a thread whose length exceeds the distance $\overline{\bar{O}_1\bar{O}_2}$ and we attach the ends of this thread to the points $\bar{O}_1$ and $\bar{O}_2$. We attach a weight to the thread in such a way that it can glide freely along the length of the thread (for instance, by passing the thread through the ringlike handle of a little weight, as shown in Fig. 7). If we now leave the weight to hang freely on the thread it will finally settle at a certain point $\bar{M}_1$ where it will be in a state of rest. It is clear that we have the following two facts:

(C_1) <u>The plane $\overline{\bar{O}_1\bar{O}_2\bar{M}}$ is vertical</u> (i.e. passes through a vertical straight line).

(C_2) <u>The angles formed by the segments $\overline{\bar{M}\bar{O}_1}$, and $\overline{\bar{M}}$ $\bar{O}_2$ with the horizontal straight line drawn through the point $\bar{M}$ in the plane $\bar{M}$ $\overline{\bar{O}_1\bar{O}_2}$ are equal.</u>

Let us note, that the propositions $(\bar{C}_1)$ and $(\bar{C}_2)$ can be deduced from the proposition about the uniqueness of the position of equilibrium of the weight. For this purpose, let us draw a vertical straight line through the midpoint of the segment $\overline{\bar{O}_1\bar{O}_2}$ and let us turn our thread, to-

PROBLEM ON A TANGENT TO AN ELLIPSE

gether with the weight, through 180° about that vertical straight line. The end $\bar{O}_1$ of the thread will turn out to be at $\bar{O}_2$ and the end $\bar{O}_2$ at $\bar{O}_1$. According to the proposition (S) of the preceding section, we shall obtain a state of equilibrium; on the grounds of the proposed uniqueness of that position, therefore, the thread (and also the triangle $\overline{M}\,\overline{O}_1\overline{O}_2$) will coincide with its previous position. When a triangle, on being rotated through 180°, coincides with itself, it means that the axis of rotation lies in the plane of the triangle. This means that the plane $\overline{M}\overline{O}_1\overline{O}_2$ passes through the vertical axis, i.e. is vertical. Furthermore, in the rotation thus carried out the horizontal straight line drawn through $\overline{M}$ in the plane $\overline{M}\,\overline{O}_1\overline{O}_2$ will coincide with itself, and the angle formed by it with the segment $\overline{M}\overline{O}_1$ will coincide with the angle formed by it with the segment $\overline{M}\,\overline{O}_2$. This means that these angles are equal.

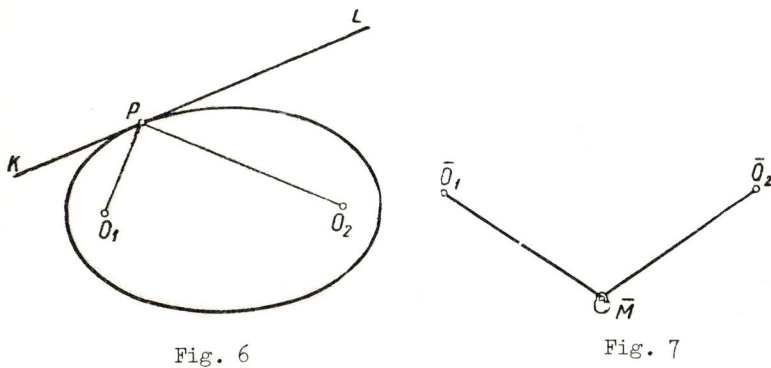

Fig. 6   Fig. 7

We now get rid of the supposition that the points of suspension are both situated at the same height. Let O_1 and O_2 be any points. Let us suspend from them a weight freely gliding along a thread (Fig. 8). Let the weight be at point M when it is at rest. Note that if the weight is at M and if we fasten the thread at any point along it the position of the weight will not change. If we fasten the thread at point $\bar{O}_2$ (see Fig. 8), the tension in the portion $\bar{O}_2 O_2$ of the thread will be replaced by the reaction of the support at point $\bar{O}_2$. This circumstance permits us to extend to the more general case the conclusions arrived at by examining the case of points of suspension at equal heights. Indeed, it is sufficient to fasten the thread at point $\bar{O}_2$ situated at the same height as O_1 (Fig. 8)*.

---

*In the drawing O_2 is higher than O_1; the case when O_1 is higher than O_2 can be discussed in a similar manner.

Putting $\bar{O}_1 = O_1$ we arrive at the previously discussed case of points $\bar{O}_1$ and $\bar{O}_2$ at equal heights. The propositions $(\bar{C}_1)$ and $(\bar{C}_2)$ therefore give rise immediately to propositions (C_1) (self-evident) and (C_2).

(C_1) <u>The plane $O_1 O_2 M$ is vertical.</u>

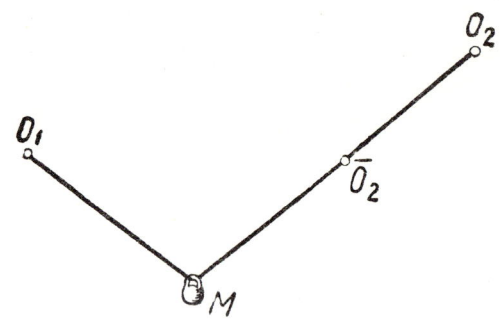

Fig. 8

(C_2) <u>The angles formed by segments MO_1 and MO_2 with a horizontal straight line drawn through the point M in the plane $MO_1 O_2$ are equal.</u>

Finally, the following two statements are also self-evidently true.

(A) <u>In the position of equilibrium the weight occupies the lowest of all positions which it can occupy while attached to the thread.</u> (This statement is deducible from the uniqueness of the position of equilibrium with the help of the principle of minimum of potential energy mentioned in Section **1.**)

(B) <u>In the position of equilibrium the thread is fully stretched.</u> (This means that the segments MO_1 and MO_2 of the thread are rectilinear and therefore the sum of distances from point M to O_1 and O_2 equals the length of the thread.)

We return to the proof of our theorem about the tangent. Suppose we are given an ellipse with foci O_1 and O_2 (Fig. 6) and length of major axis l, and a straight line KL, touching it at the point P. It is required to prove that

PROBLEM ON A TANGENT TO AN ELLIPSE

$\angle O_1PK = \angle O_2PL$. To prove this, let us turn the drawing in such a way that its plane becomes vertical, the straight line *KL* becomes horizontal and the ellipse is situated above the straight line *KL* (then *P* will be the lowest point on the ellipse). Let us take a thread of length *l* and thread a weight on to it. Let us fasten the ends of the thread at points O_1 and O_2 after which we let the weight hang freely. It takes up a certain position *M*. In accordance with (C_1), the point *M* will lie in the plane of the drawing. In accordance with (B) it will lie on the ellipse. In accordance with (A) it will coincide with *P*. Thus, the thread will follow the segments PO_1 and PO_2. In accordance with (C_2), the angles formed by these segments with the straight line *KL* are equal.

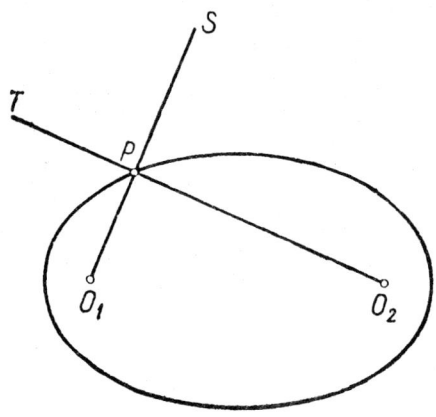

Fig. 9

The property that a tangent to an ellipse forms equal angles with the focal radii allows us to construct a tangent to an ellipse at a given point using compasses and a ruler (given the foci of the ellipse). For this, it is sufficient to draw straight lines through the point of contact *P* and the foci O_1 and O_2 (Fig. 9) and find the bisector of angle SPO_2 (or of the angle TPO_1). This bisector is the tangent.

SOME APPLICATIONS OF MECHANICS TO MATHEMATICS

The theorem about a tangent to an ellipse has an interesting optical interpretation; if we regard the ellipse as being "mirrorlike" the rays issuing from a point-source of light placed in one of the foci will converge at the other focus (Fig. 10).

Indeed, the angle formed by the incident ray with the ellipse equals the angle formed by the reflected ray with the ellipse, according to the laws of optics. The angle formed by a straight line and a curve (in this case by the ray of light and the ellipse) is measured by the angle between this straight line and the tangent to the curve drawn at the vertex of the angle. In so far as the incident ray follows one focal radius according to the theorem just proved, the reflected ray will follows another focal radius.

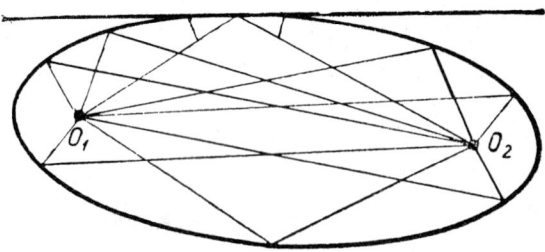

Fig. 10

3. PROBLEMS ON TANGENTS TO PARABOLAS AND HYPERBOLAS

A <u>parabola</u> (Fig. 11) is the name given to the locus of a point P, equidistant from a certain point F (called the focus of the parabola) and from a certain straight line d called the <u>directrix</u> of the parabola.

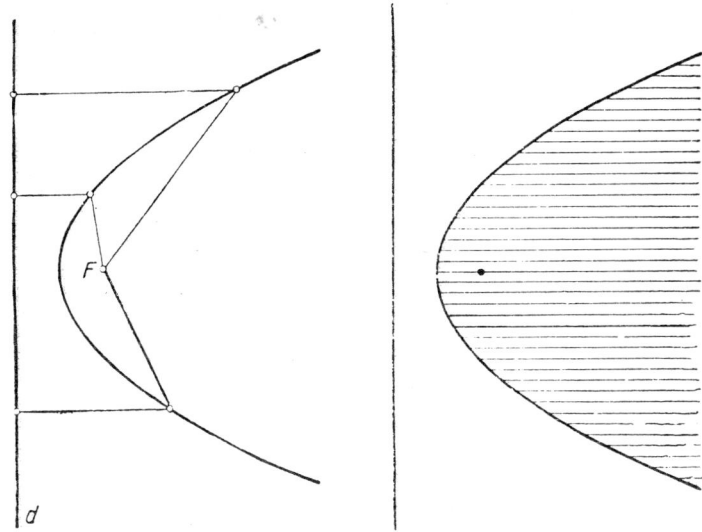

Fig. 11   Fig. 12

A parabola divides the plane into two parts: one contains the directrix, the other (shaded in in Fig. 12) contains the focus. A straight line having exactly one point in common with the parabola and lying wholly in one part into which the parabola divides the plane is called a tangent to the parabola. In Fig. 13 the straight line p is a tangent to the parabola, but the straight line q is not a tangent although it has only one point in common with it.

We have the following theorem relating to a tangent to the parabola: <u>If from any point P on the parabola we draw a segment PF joining P to the focus, and a segment PD perpendicular to the directrix, then the angles formed by these segments with the tangent p at point P are equal</u> (thus, in Fig. 14 $\angle DPK = \angle KPF$).

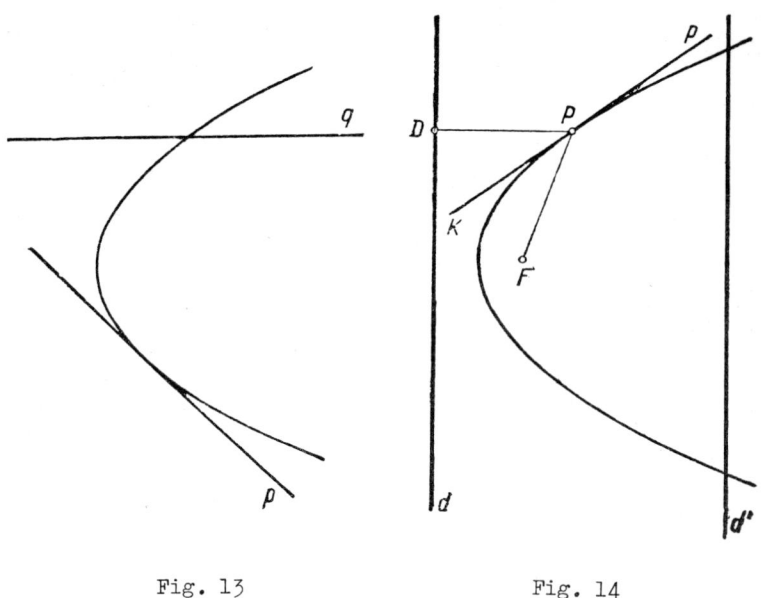

Fig. 13   Fig. 14

This theorem can be "proved" by means of "mechanical" considerations in a similar way to the theorems in the two previous sections. We shall outline such a "proof".

At an arbitrary distance l from d we draw a straight line d' parallel to d, such, that the point P lies between d and d'. Let us turn the drawing until it is in a vertical plane in such a way that the tangent p is horizontal and the parabola is situated above p. Let us imagine the straight line d' as a thin rod with a ring sliding on it (Fig. 15). We attach a thread of length l to the ring. We fasten the other end of the thread at the point F. We shall thread the thread through a weight, so that the weight can slide along the thread. Let the position of equilibrium of the weight be *M*, and the position of the ring at the same time be *D'*. The thread is taut, and therefore the segments *MF* and *MD'* of the thread are rectilinear. First, we note that

$$MD' \perp d'. \tag{1}$$

(If this were not so, then, as seen in Fig. 16, the component T_1 of the tension *T* down the rod *d'* would be non-zero,

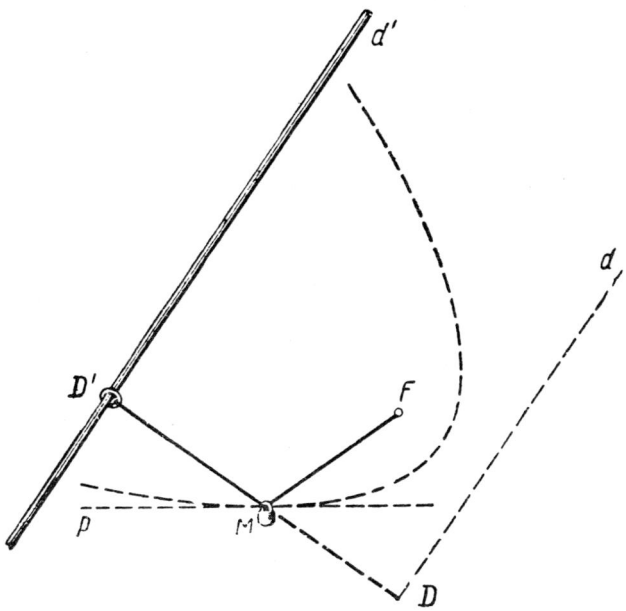

Fig. 15

and would make the ring move.) Further, repeating the reasoning of the preceding section, we establish in the first place that the angles formed by segments *MD'* and *MF* with the straight line *p* are equal, and in the second place that

$$MD' + MF = l. \tag{2}$$

Let us draw *MD* perpendicular to *d*. Since the distance

between d and d' equals l, then it follows from (1) and (2) that

$$MD = MF. \qquad (3)$$

This means that M lies on the parabola, and in so far as M occupies the lowest of possible positions and P is the lowest point on the parabola, M coincides with P. In the

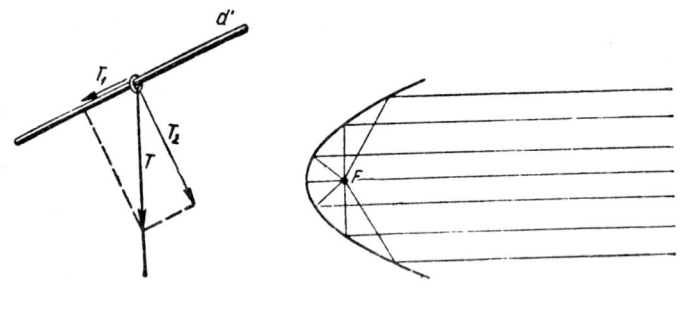

Fig. 16   Fig. 17

final count, therefore, the angles formed by segments PF and PD with the straight line p are equal.

The property of the angles formed by a tangent to a parabola enables the tangent to be constructed by means of a ruler and compasses.

The optical interpretation of the theorem just proved is as follows. Rays of light originating at the focus of a parabola, when reflected from the parabola, are transformed into a beam of rays perpendicular to the directrix (Fig. 17). This property of the parabola is utilized in projectors, reflectors and other apparatus serving to direct rays (light or heat) in a desired direction. The reflecting surface of any such apparatus is the surface generated by rotating a parabola about the perpendicular from the focus to the directrix.

A hyperbola is the name of the locus of a point the difference of whose distances from two fixed points F_1 and F_2 (called foci) is constant. A hyperbola, as is seen in Fig. 18, consists of two branches. The distance from any point P' on the left branch (in Fig. 18) to F_1 is <u>less</u> by the fixed amount than the distance from P' to F_2; the

PROBLEMS ON TANGENTS TO PARABOLAS AND HYPERBOLAS   15

distance from any point P'' on the right branch to F_2 is <u>less</u> by the same amount than the distance from P'' to F_1. In the same way as the parabola each branch of the hyperbola divides the plane into two parts. A straight line situated wholly in one part of the plane and having exactly one point in common with one of the branches of the hyperbola is called a <u>tangent to that branch of the hyperbola</u>. In Fig. 19 a straight line is shown which is a tangent to the left branch of the hyperbola at point P. It is possible to prove that

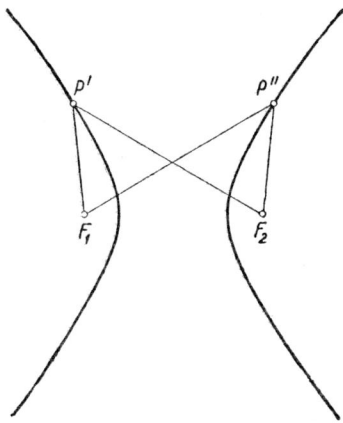

Fig. 18

a tangent to one of the branches of the hyperbola does not intersect the other branch. Any tangent to either of the branches of the hyperbola is simply called a <u>tangent to the hyperbola</u>.

Just as in the case of the ellipse, rectilinear segments joining the focus with a point on the hyperbola are called <u>focal radii</u>.

We have the following theorem concerning a tangent to a hyperbola: <u>a tangent to a hyperbola forms equal angles with the focal radii drawn at the point of contact</u>. (Thus in Fig. 19 $\angle F_1PL = \angle LPF_2$.) We shall not give a proof of this theorem (we leave it to the reader); we shall just show the "mechanical" construction which forms the basis of it. From the definition of the hyperbola we know that the difference between the focal radii is constant. Let us denote this difference by a. Let the point of contact P lie on the right branch (Fig. 20). From the left focus F_1 we draw a circle of a sufficiently large radius r so that, firstly $r > a$, and secondly the point lies inside this circle. We shall imagine the circle as made up of wire with a small ring sliding along it. We take a thread of length $r-a$ and let us thread it through a weight which can slide along it. We fasten one end of the thread to the small ring, and we

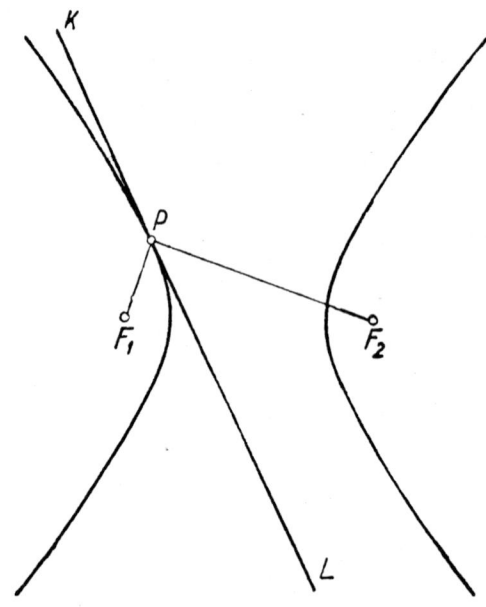

Fig. 19

fasten the other end at the right focus F_2. If we now turn the drawing in such a way that the straight line p (the tangent) is horizontal and the corresponding branch of the hyperbola is above the straight line p, the weight on the thread will be situated at point P. This circumstance enables us to prove this theorem with the aid of reasoning previously applied. We note that, if the point of contact lies on the left branch, the construction can be repeated by drawing the circle from the right focus. It is possible, however, in this case to use a circle with centre at the left focus, but the thread must then be of the length $r + a$.

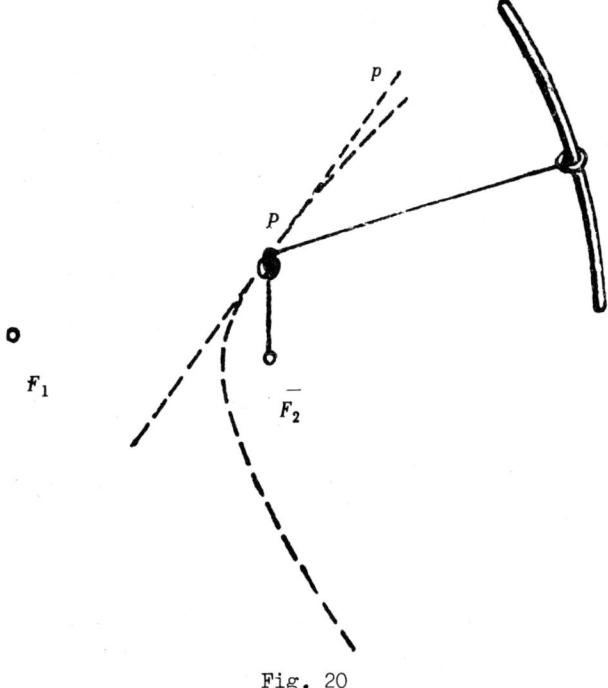

Fig. 20

Just as in the case of the preceding theorems on tangents, the theorem on a tangent to a hyperbola gives a practical method of constructing tangents.

4. PRINCIPLE OF LEAST POTENTIAL ENERGY

A weight raised to some height is capable of doing some work in falling, i.e. it possesses potential energy. As is known from a school course of physics, the potential energy of a weight q raised to a height h is measured by the product qh. We see that the lower the weight, the smaller is its potential energy. The tendency of the weight to take up the lowest position is connected with the fact that the weight tries to make its potential energy as small as possible. If the weight is fastened to a thread the potential energy is minimal at the lowest position it can take up. Statement (A), which has played a decisive part in proving the theorems on tangents and which states that the weight occupies the lowest possible position when it is in a position of equilibrium, is therefore equivalent to the following proposition:

(U) <u>In the position of equilibrium the potential energy of the weight reaches its least value</u>.

In its turn, the proposition (U) (and so also (A)) is a corollary of the proposition (E) about the uniqueness of the position of equilibrium and of the following proposition:

(D') <u>If, when the weight occupies a certain position, its potential energy reaches its least value, that position is its position of equilibrium</u>.

To deduce (U) from this, it is sufficient to note that if the potential energy were not to reach its least value at the position of equilibrium there would exist, on the basis of (D'), another position of equilibrium corresponding to the least value of the potential energy; but this contradicts the proposition (E).

Statement (D') is a particular instance of a general principle in mechanics called the principle of minimum of potential energy, or the principle of Dirichlet.

PRINCIPLE OF LEAST POTENTIAL ENERGY

Dirichlet's principle states:

<u>That position of a system in which potential energy reaches its least value is the position of equilibrium.</u>

If the position of equilibrium is unique then Dirichlet's principle gives rise to an important corollary:

<u>In the position of equilibrium the potential energy of a system reaches its least value.</u>

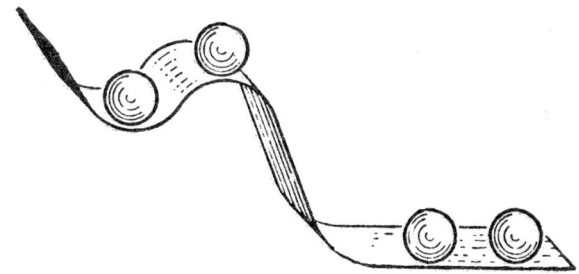

Fig. 21

The proof of this corollary is similar to the proof of proposition (U).

Further on we shall examine only cases where the position of equilibrium is unique. (It is possible for it to be otherwise; thus, in Fig. 21, four positions of equilibrium of a sphere are shown.)

It is not, of course, necessary to apply the principle of minimum potential energy to the solution of problems on tangents. The fact that the weight occupies the lowest of all possible positions is self-evident. In other cases, however, when we are dealing with several weights tied to each other, it would be untrue to state that in the position of equilibrium each of them occupies the lowest of all geometrically possible positions. Here it is necessary to find the positions of all weights and for this it is often convenient to make use of the concept of potential energy.

Let us demonstrate by an example.

The remarkable book of the Polish mathematician Steinhaus, 'Mathematical Kaleidoscope', contains the following problem (Theme 39).

'It is required to build a common school for three villages. There are 50 children in the first village, 70 children in the second and 90 children in the third village. Where should the school be situated for the sum of the time expended by the children on getting to school to be minimal?'

To solve this problem it is sufficient to place a plan of the locality on a table (Fig. 22), then drill holes in the table at the points where the villages are situated, pass thin strings through these holes, tie the top ends of these three strings in one knot, and at the lower ends hang loads of 50, 70 and 90 units respectively (e.g. 500, 700 and 900 gm). The school should be built at the spot where the knot settles. (Why?)

In order to answer the question 'why?' set in this problem we add up the potential energy of the system, consisting in this case of three weights. If the weights are q_1, q_2 and q_3 and if the first weight is at height h_1, the second at height h_2 and the third at height h_3 then the potential energy equals the sum of potential energies of the separate weights*.

$$E = q_1 h_1 + q_2 h_2 + q_3 h_3. \qquad (1)$$

Now, let r_1, r_2, r_3 be the distances from the knot to the first, second and third village respectively; l_1, l_2 and l_3 the lengths of first, second and third strings and h the height of the surface of the table. Obviously, at whatever point the knot is situated and whatever the heights of the weights, we have the following relations:

$$r_1 + (h - h_1) = l_1, \quad r_2 + (h - h_2) = l_2, \quad r_3 + (h - h_3) = l_3$$

---

*Indeed, potential energy is measured by the work which can be carried out. If the strings were cut on falling, each weight will carry out work equal to its potential energy, and the whole system will carry out work equal to the sum of all these separate works.

PRINCIPLE OF LEAST POTENTIAL ENERGY 21

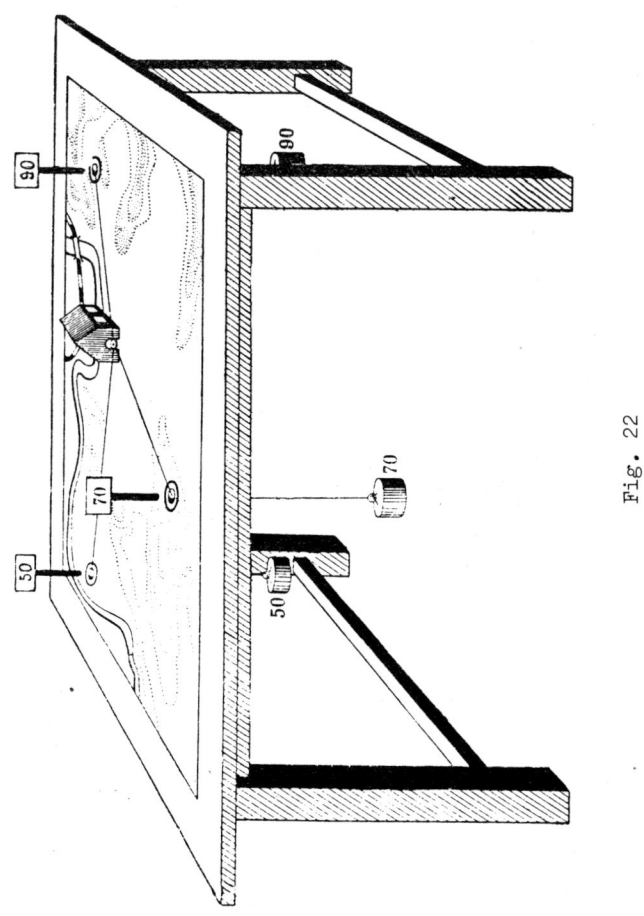

Fig. 22

or
$$h_1 = r_1 + h - l_1, \quad h_2 = r_2 + h - l_2, \quad h_3 = r_3 + h - l_3$$

Then the equation (1) can be rewritten thus:
$$E = q_1 r_1 + q_2 r_2 + q_3 r_3 + C,$$
where
$$C = (q_1 + q_2 + q)h - q_1 l_1 - q_2 l_2 - q\, l_3$$

is a constant quantity, independent of the position of the weights.

From the principle of minimum potential energy, when E is at its smallest, the system is in equilibrium. Hence (and presupposing the uniqueness of the position of equilibrium) it follows that in the state of equilibrium the value of E is minimal. But if the value of E is minimal then the quantity
$$T = q_1 r_1 + q_2 r_2 + q_3 r_3 = E - C$$

is also minimal. But T is just that total time which is used by the children in getting from their villages to the school situated at the knot. So that in the position of the knot corresponding to the equilibrium of the system this sum of time does reach its minimum value.

5. MATERIAL POINTS AND THE CENTRE OF GRAVITY

Until now, we have said nothing about the dimensions of the weights which were being suspended by threads. From the reasoning which was employed it is seen on one hand that we supposed the weights to be very small in size (so small that the position of each could be regarded as a point) on the other hand, we endowed them with definite weights, and so, masses.

Such considerations lead us to one of the fundamental ideas in mechanics - the idea of a material point.

In mechanics a material point is understood to be a body so small that its dimensions can be ignored. A material point can be visualized as a geometric point, which has a particular number (its 'mass') ascribed to it.

In any system of material points, each point experiences the action of the force of gravity proportional to the mass of the point. The resultant of all these parallel forces acts on a special point, called the centre of gravity of the given system of material points. The position of the centre of gravity depends on the positions of the points of the system and their masses.

In mechanics a body is regarded as consisting of a large number of material points. These material points in general have different masses, so that the distribution of mass inside a body is uneven; some parts of the body have a larger mass; some have a smaller mass. We shall even suppose separate parts of a body not to have any mass and be therefore 'weightless'*. The centre of gravity of the system of

---

*More exactly, by a 'weightless body' (or a body with 'zero mass') we understand a body whose mass is so small that it can be neglected. The reader might notice a parallel between the concept of a material point and the concept of a weightless body. The neglecting of the mass of a body plays no less an important part in mechanics than the

material points making up the body is, by definition, the centre of gravity of the body itself. If the mass of the body is concentrated in a finite number of its separate points (we shall come across such cases further on, for example, the case of a weightless rod with point loads attached to it) then the centre of gravity of such a body obviously coincides with the centre of gravity of the system of these separate points. Many properties of a body

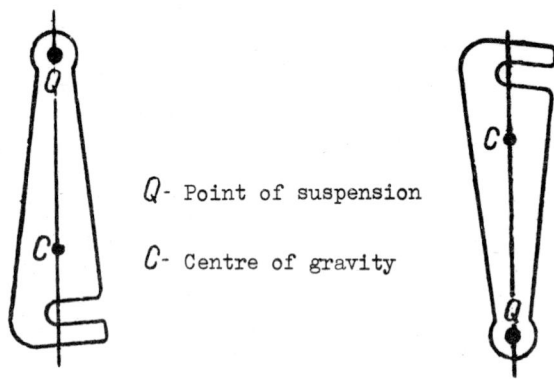

Q - Point of suspension

C - Centre of gravity

Fig. 23

depend entirely on the position of its centre of gravity. As is known from a school course in physics, the equilibrium of a body depends on the mutual distribution of its centre of gravity and of a multiplicity of points at which the body is fastened. In fact, we have the following propositions:

Proposition 1. <u>If a body attached to a fixed point is at rest, that point and the centre of gravity of the body are on the same vertical line</u> (Fig. 23).

Proposition 2. <u>If a body which has an area of support or an edge of support is at rest, then a vertical line drawn from the centre of gravity downwards intersects this area or edge</u> (Fig. 24).

---

neglecting of size. Thus, in all the preceding discussions we have been neglecting the weight (but not the **dimensions**) of the threads.

These propositions can be used to find the centre of gravity experimentally.

In particular, the following result follows from these propositions: if a body is replaced by a body of the same shape and the same centre of gravity then the position of equilibrium remains the same. In many cases, however, it is necessary to take into account, not only the centre of gravity, but also the general mass of the body (i.e. the

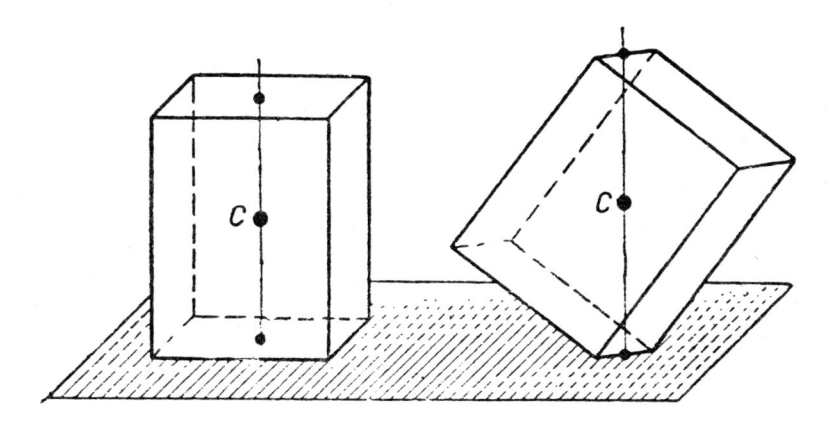

Fig. 24

sum of the masses of the material points making up the body). For instance, if we interchange not the whole body, but a part of it, by some other body having the same shape and the same centre of gravity as the part to be interchanged, then the equilibrium of the whole body may be affected, since the position of the centre of gravity of the whole body may change on account of the change in mass of its part. A knowledge of the position of the centre of gravity and the total mass of the body is quite sufficient in solving many problems - at least in solving all the problems with which we are to meet later. It is natural, therefore, to introduce the following definition of the equivalence of two systems of material points. <u>Two systems of material points are equivalent, if, firstly, the centre of gravity of the first coincides with the centre of gravity of the second system and, secondly, the sum of the masses of</u>

all points of the first system equals the sum of the masses of all points of the second system. The concept of equivalence of systems introduced here is remarkable in this way: when replacing a part of a certain system by a system equivalent to this part, we arrive at a system equivalent to the initial one. Let us try to state this proposition in a clearer form.

Suppose we are given a system $\bar{\alpha}$ of material points $\bar{M}_1, \ldots, \bar{M}_r$ of masses $\bar{m}_1, \ldots, \bar{m}_r$ and a system $\underline{\alpha}$ of material points $\underline{M}_1, \ldots, \underline{M}_s$ of masses $\underline{m}_1, \ldots, \underline{m}_s$. Let us join both these systems into one general system α, which we determine in the following manner:

(1) We shall include in α every material point of the system $\bar{\alpha}$ which does not coincide in position with any points of the system $\underline{\alpha}$.

(2) We include in α every material point of the system $\underline{\alpha}$ which does not coincide in position with any points of the system $\bar{\alpha}$.

(3) If a certain material point $\bar{M}_i$ of the system $\bar{\alpha}$ coincides in position with a certain material point $\underline{M}_j$ of the system $\underline{\alpha}$, we shall include in α a new material point, whose position coincides with those of the material points $\bar{M}_i$ and $\underline{M}_j$ and whose mass equals the sum $\bar{m}_i + \underline{m}_j$ of the masses of the above-mentioned material points. We then have:

> Proposition 3. If the system α is a result of joining the systems $\bar{\alpha}$ and $\underline{\alpha}$ and the system β is a result of joining the systems $\bar{\beta}$ and $\underline{\beta}$, and if the systems $\bar{\alpha}$ and $\bar{\beta}$ are equivalent and the systems $\underline{\alpha}$ and $\underline{\beta}$ are equivalent, the systems α and β are also equivalent.

The proof of proposition 3. The fact that the sum-masses of systems α and β are identical is obvious. We shall show that the centres of gravity of these systems also coincide. The resultant of all the forces of gravity acting on the material points of the system α can be found as follows: first we find the resultant $\bar{P}$ of the forces of gravity acting on $\bar{\alpha}$, then we find the resultant $\underline{P}$ of the forces of gravity acting on $\underline{\alpha}$ and finally we find the resultant P of these resultants. In the same way the resultant Q of the forces of gravity acting on the system β can be found as the resultant of two forces $\bar{Q}$ and $\underline{Q}$, where $\bar{Q}$ is the resultant of forces acting on $\bar{\beta}$ and $\underline{Q}$ is the resultant of forces acting on β. Since $\bar{\alpha}$ and $\bar{\beta}$ are equivalent the forces $\bar{P}$ and $\bar{Q}$ are identical. In the same way the forces P and Q are identical. Their resultants, therefore, also coincide. In particular the points at which they act, i.e. the centres of gravity of systems α and β, coincide.

Note that for any system of material points it is possible to construct a system equivalent to it and consisting of only one material point. For this it is sufficient to consider a material point situated at the centre of gravity of the original system and having mass equal to the sum of the masses of the system. This material point forms the system equivalent to the original ones. A material point situated at the centre of gravity of a certain system and having a mass equal to the sum of the masses of that system is called the <u>material centre</u> of the given system. Equivalent systems can be defined as systems whose material centres coincide.

6. THE CENTRE OF GRAVITY OF A SYSTEM OF TWO MATERIAL POINTS

Suppose that two loads P and Q are attached to a weightless rod at a distance d from each other (Fig. 25). It is required to find the centre of gravity of the rod together with the loads. From proposition 1 in the previous section we see that our problem is equivalent to that of finding at which point O should the rod be supported in order to be in equilibrium. Let us denote the distances of the loads P and Q from the required point O by u and v. Equilibrium

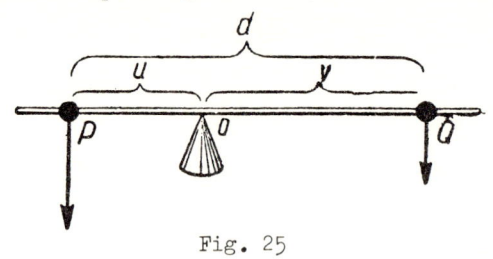

Fig. 25

is reached when and only when the product of the force P and the distance u equals the product of the force Q and the distance v, i.e.

$$Pu = Qv. \qquad (1)$$

Comparing equation (1) with the equation

$$u + v = d, \qquad (2)$$

we get

$$u = \frac{Q}{P+Q}d, \quad v = \frac{P}{P+Q}d.$$

Note that $\frac{u}{v} = \frac{Q}{P}$, so that distances from the centre of gravity to the loads are inversely proportional to the loads themselves.

28

SYSTEM OF TWO MATERIAL POINTS

In particular, if both loads are of equal weights, the centre of gravity is situated midway between the loads (which is obvious straightaway) and conversely, if it is known that the centre of gravity is at mid-point, then it follows that the loads are equal.

If one of the loads is twice as heavy as the other then the centre of gravity is nearer the heavier load and divides the distance between the loads in a ratio 1:2, conversely, if it is known that the centre of gravity divides the distance between the loads in a ratio 1:2, then one of the loads (namely, the one nearer the centre of gravity) is twice as big as the other.

In as much as the centre of gravity of a rod whose mass is concentrated at two points M and N coincides with the centre of gravity of a system of two material points M and N (with corresponding masses), we have obtained the following result:

The centre of gravity of a system of two material points lies on the straight line joining these points. Its distances from these points are inversely proportional to the weights of these points (that means also to their masses).

In particular, the centre of gravity bisects the distance between two points when, and only when, both points have equal weights; the centre of gravity divides the distance between points in the ratio 1:2 when, and only when, one of these points is twice as heavy as the other (the centre of gravity being nearer the heavier point).

7. THEOREMS ABOUT THE INTERSECTION OF STRAIGHT LINES

We now consider any system of material points α, which is the union of systems γ and δ. We denote the material centres of γ and δ by M and N. From Proposition 3 of Section 5, the system of material points M and N is equivalent to the system α. Therefore the material centre of system α coincides with the material centre of the system consisting of points M and N, and therefore it lies on the straight line joining these points. In as much as the material centre of a system is situated at its centre of gravity, we obtain the following theorem:

The centre of gravity of a system of material points which is formed by the union of systems γ and δ lies on the straight line joining the centres of gravity of systems γ and δ.

We shall now give three geometrical applications of this theorem.

The medians of a triangle are concurrent. Let us place equal point loads at the vertices of a triangle. Let the loads be denoted by the same letters A, B, C as the vertices (Fig. 26). We shall partition the system of material points thus obtained into two parts γ and δ in such a way that A should belong to γ and B and C to δ. The centre of gravity of γ is at A and the centre of gravity of δ is at the midpoint E of the side BC, as it follows from results obtained in the previous section. According to the theorem established at the beginning of this section, the centre of gravity O of the system A, B, C lies on the median AE. In a completely similar manner we can convince ourselves that O lies also on the other two medians. And so all three medians concur.

Since the material centre M of the system (to be found at point E) is twice as heavy as the material centre of the centre of the system γ, which coincides with the point A, the centre of gravity of the system $\{M, A\}$ divides the

THEOREMS ABOUT THE INTERSECTION OF STRAIGHT LINES

segment *EA* in the ratio 1:2, it itself being nearer *E*. But this centre of gravity is the centre of gravity of the system *A*, *B*, *C*, i.e. the common point of intersection of all the medians. We have thus obtained the well-known theorem about the point of intersection of the medians cutting off a third of each median counting from the corresponding side.

Space quadrilateral. Suppose we have a space quadrilateral *ABCD* (Fig. 27). We shall show that the straight lines *EF* and *KL* joining the mid-points of its opposite sides intersect. We place equal weights at the vertices of the quadrilateral. We regard these weights as material points. Just

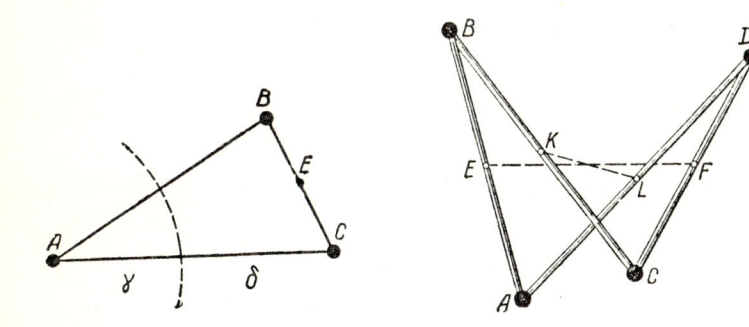

Fig. 26   Fig. 27

as in the 'proof' of the theorem about the medians it is sufficient to discover that the centre of gravity of the quadrilateral lies on each of the straight lines *EF* and *KL*. Let us show, for instance, that it lies on *EF* (the fact, that it lies on *KL*, is shown in a similar manner). In order to do that, we partition the system of material points *A, B, C, D* into two parts, we include points *A* and *B* into one of them, and points *C* and *D* into the other. The centre of gravity of the first part will be situated at the point *E*, the centre of gravity of the second part will be at point *F*. On the basis of the theorem formulated at the beginning of this section, the centre of gravity of the whole quadrilateral is situated on the straight line *EF*. It is left to the reader to prove that the segments *EF* and *KL* bisect each other at their point of intersection.

Ceva's theorem. The theorem about the concurrence of the

medians of a triangle is a particular case of the following proposition known as the theorem of Ceva:

Let A_1, B_1, C_1 be three points lying on sides BC, CA and AB of the triangle ABC (Fig. 28). In order that the straight lines AA_1, BB_1, CC_1 should be concurrent, it is necessary and sufficient that the relation

$$\frac{AB_1}{B_1C} \cdot \frac{CA_1}{A_1B} \cdot \frac{BC_1}{C_1A} = 1 \qquad (1)$$

be satisfied.

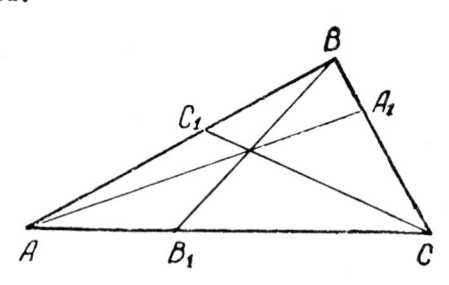

Fig. 28

It is recommended that the reader verifies that the relation (1) does really hold in the following cases:

1. When the straight lines AA_1, BB_1, CC_1 are bisectors of the triangle. (<u>Hint</u>: use the theorem that states that the bisector of an angle in a triangle divides the opposite side into parts proportional to the adjacent sides). Hence it follows that the bisectors of a triangle are concurrent.

2. When the straight lines AA_1, BB_1, CC_1 are the altitudes of a triangle (<u>Hint</u>: use the formula which expresses the lengths of the segments into which the altitude divides the corresponding side). Hence it follows that the altitudes of a triangle are concurrent.

We pass on to the proof of Ceva's theorem.

Suppose that the relation (1) is valid. We shall show that the straight lines AA_1, BB_1, CC_1 are concurrent. The reasoning follows the same course as in the two preceding 'proofs'. We shall show that, with appropriately selected loads placed at the vertices, the centre of gravity of the system lies on each of the straight lines AA_1, BB_1, CC_1. Let (to any scale)

$$AB_1 = a, \quad B_1C = b,$$
$$CA_1 = c, \quad A_1B = d,$$
$$BC_1 = e, \quad C_1A = f,$$

so that

$$\frac{a}{b} \cdot \frac{c}{d} \cdot \frac{e}{f} = 1. \qquad (2)$$

At the vertex A we place a load equal to bd, at the vertex B - a load equal to ac, at the vertex C - a load equal to ad. The centre of gravity of the system $\{A, C\}$ lies at a point whose distances from the vertices A and C are inversely proportional to the loads at these vertices; but B_1 is such a point. In the same way, the centre of gravity of the system $\{B, C\}$ lies at the point A_1. Finally, the centre of gravity of the system $\{A, B\}$ lies at a point whose distances x and y from the vertices A and B are inversely proportional to the loads bd and ac, i.e.

$$\frac{x}{y} = \frac{ac}{bd} \text{ and } x+y = f+e.$$

But from the relationship (2) it follows that

$$\frac{ac}{bd} = \frac{f}{e}$$

Therefore $x = f, y = e$. It follows that the centre of gravity of the system $\{A, B\}$ falls at the point C_1. It remains to be noted that, by the theorem quoted at the beginning of this section, the centre of gravity of the whole triangle lies on each of the straight lines AA_1, BB_1, CC_1.

Conversely, let the straight lines AA_1, BB_1, CC_1 concur at the point O; we shall show that the relation (1) then holds. To show this, we imagine our triangle as a weightless lamina; we position it horizontally, support it at O and place loads at vertices in such a way as to keep the triangle in equilibrium (Fig. 29). From the proposition 1 in Section 5, the point O is the centre of gravity of the triangle with the loads, which have been selected as indicated, at the vertices, and so, it is the centre of gravity of the system of these loads. Therefore the point O should lie on the straight line joining A with the centre of gravity of the system $\{B, C\}$, and therefore A_1 is the centre of gravity of the system $\{B, C\}$. In the same way B_1 and C_1 are the centres of gravity of systems $\{C, A\}$ and $\{A, B\}$. If

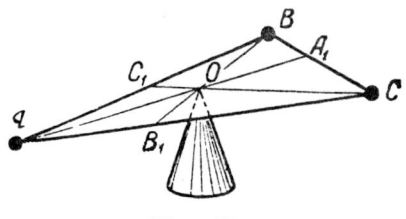

Fig. 29

the masses of material points A, B, C are denoted by p, q and r respectively, then, according to the preceding section

$$\frac{AB_1}{B_1C} = \frac{r}{p}, \quad \frac{CA_1}{A_1B} = \frac{q}{r}, \quad \frac{BC_1}{C_1P} = \frac{p}{q}.$$

Multiplying all these proportions we obtain the required relation (1).

8. THE CENTRE OF GRAVITY OF A ROD WITH MANY LOADS

We now generalize the considerations of Section 6.

Let us now imagine a weightless rod (Fig. 30) with loads of weights $P_1, P_2, ..., P_n$ fixed on it, and pose the problem of finding the centre of gravity of this rod. Just as in Section 6 in order to solve the problem it is sufficient to find a point O, such that, if the rod were supported at that point, it would be in equilibrium. We calculate the abscissa x of such a point of support*.

Let the abscissa of the load P_1 equal a_1, the abscissa of the load P_2 equal a_2, etc., and finally the abscissa of the load P_n equal a_n. Suppose (Fig. 30) that the point of support O is situated between the loads P_k and P_{k+1} (the case when one of these loads is situated exactly at O is not excluded). Then the arms of the forces $P_1, ..., P_k$ are equal to $x-a_1, ..., x-a_k$ respectively, and the arms of forces $P_{k+1}, ..., P_n$ are equal to $a_{k+1}-x, ..., a_n-x$ respectively.

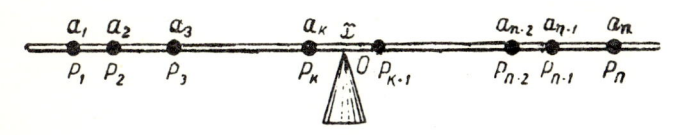

Fig. 30

Since the rod is in equilibrium, the sum of the moments about O of the forces turning the rod anticlockwise should equal the sum of moments about O of the forces turning the rod clockwise, i.e.

$$P_1(x-a_1) + ... + P_k(x-a_k) = P_{k+1}(a_{k+1}-x) + ... + P_n(a_n-x).$$

---

*The abscissa of a point on a rod is understood to be the distance of that point from the left end of the rod.

35

Transposing the terms containing x to the left hand side and all the rest to the right we find that

$$(P_1 + \ldots + P_k + P_{k+1} + \ldots + P_n)x = P_1 a_1 + \ldots + P_k a_k + P_{k+1} a_{k+1} + \ldots + P_n a_n.$$

Hence we find that

$$x = \frac{P_1 a_1 + \ldots + P_n a_n}{P_1 + \ldots + P_n}$$

<u>Example 1</u>. Let $P_1 = 1$, $P_2 = 2$, ..., $P_n = n$; $a_1 = 1$, $a_2 = 2$, ..., $a_n = n$. In this case, according to the formula just derived,

$$x = \frac{1^2 + 2^2 + \ldots + n^2}{1 + 2 + \ldots + n}$$

To simplify this expression, we write out the equalities:

$$1^3 = (1+0)^3 = 1^3,$$
$$2^3 = (1+1)^3 = 1^3 + 3 \cdot 1^2 + 3 \cdot 1 + 1,$$
$$3^3 = (2+1)^3 = 2^3 + 3 \cdot 2^2 + 3 \cdot 2 + 1,$$
$$\ldots \ldots \ldots \ldots \ldots \ldots \ldots$$
$$(n+1)^3 = (n+1)^3 = n^3 + 3 \cdot n^2 + 3 \cdot n + 1.$$

Adding up these equalities we get

$$1^3 + 2^3 + \ldots + (n+1)^3 = 1 + (1^3 + 2^3 + \ldots + n^3) +$$
$$+ 3(1^2 + 2^2 + \ldots + n^2) + 3(1 + 2 + \ldots + n) + n,$$

or

$$(n+1)^3 = 1 + 3(1^2 + 2^2 + \ldots + n^2) +$$
$$+ 3(1 + 2 + \ldots + n) + n,$$

or

$$3(1^2 + 2^2 + \ldots + n^2) = (n+1)(n^2 + 2n) -$$
$$- 3(1 + 2 + \ldots + n).$$

We divide both sides by $3(1 + 2 + \ldots + n)$. Then we get

$$\frac{1^2 + 2^2 + \ldots + n^2}{1 + 2 + \ldots + n} = \frac{(n+1)(n^2 + 2n)}{3(1 + 2 + \ldots + n)} - 1.$$

In the sum $1 + 2 + \ldots + n$ there are as many units as there

THE CENTRES OF GRAVITY OF A ROD WITH MANY LOADS 37

are shaded-in squares in Fig. 31, and the number of shaded-in squares is equal to the number of blank squares, i.e. half of all the squares in the rectangle, i.e. $\frac{n(n+1)}{2}$, therefore

$$x = \frac{1^2+2^2+\ldots+n^2}{1+2+\ldots+n} = \frac{(n+1)(n^2+2n)}{3(1+2+\ldots+n)} - 1 = \frac{(n+1)(n^2+2n)}{3\frac{n(n+1)}{2}} - 1 = \frac{2n+1}{3}.$$

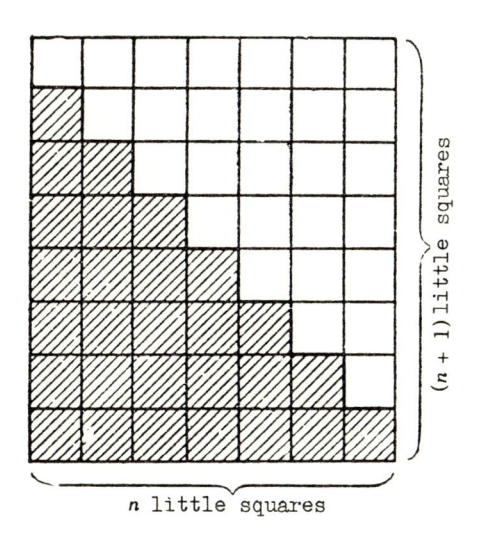

Fig. 31

Hence, by the way, we obtain the result

$$1^2+2^2+\ldots+n^2 = \frac{2n+1}{3}(1+2+\ldots+n) =$$
$$= \frac{2n+1}{3}\cdot\frac{n(n+1)}{2} = \frac{n(n+1)(2n+1)}{6}.$$

Example 2. Let the same loads as in Example 1, i.e. loads of weight 1, 2, ..., n, be situated at points whose abscissae are $1^2, 2^2, \ldots, n^2$. Prove that the abscissa of the centre of gravity is

$$\frac{n(n+1)}{2}$$

(<u>Hint</u>: Using the result of Example 1, calculate the sum of cubes $1^3+2^3+\ldots+n^3$.)

Example 3. At the same points as in example 1, i.e. points with abscissae $1, 2, ..., n$ let there be placed loads of weights $1^2, 2^2, ..., n^2$. Prove that the abscissa of the centre of gravity is

$$\frac{3n(n+1)}{2(2n+1)}.$$

9. A PROBLEM IN THE THEORY OF NUMBERS (FORMULATION)

Mechanical considerations sometimes help in solving not only geometrical but also arithmetical problems. One quite unexpected example* of this kind will be considered now.

Let us take a row of positive numbers $P_1, P_2, ..., P_n$; in order to reduce its length we subtract from each of its end-terms P_1 and P_n a number P equal to the smaller of these end-terms, and instead we add P to the middle terms (if there is only one middle term then the numbers $2P$ is added to this one term). In this process (provided $n > 2$) one or both of the end-terms become zero, therefore the row thus obtained is already shorter than the original row. Thus, for instance, if the original row had the form

$$1, 9, 3, 4,$$

we obtain the row

$$10, 4, 3.$$

If the initial row had the form

$$6, 2, 6$$

we obtain a row consisting of one number only, namely

$$14.$$

The shortened row obtained in this way will be said to be derived from the original one. Thus, the row 10, 4, 3 is derived from the row 1, 9, 3, 4, and the row 14 is derived from the row 6, 2, 6. Note that the derived row of a row

---

*This example was kindly communicated to the author by P.S. Novikov.

consisting of two numbers coincides with the row itself.

Let us now write down some row α and proceed as follows. We find the derived row of this row and denote it by α'. Further, we find the derived row of the row α'. This new row is denoted by α" and is called the second derived row of row α. The row derived from α" is called the third derived row of σ and is denoted α'" and in general the row derived from the $(n-1)$-th row we call the n-th derived row and we denote it $α^{(n)}$. In as much as the length of each derived row is less by 1 or 2 terms than the length of the preceding one, therefore, in the process of working out the consecutive derived rows for the row α, we finally arrive at a row, whose length is one or two terms; we shall call this line the last derived row or the characteristic of row α. Thus, the characteristic of row 1, 9, 3, 4 is the row 7, 10.

Note, that in passing from a row to its derived row, the sum of all terms of the row remains unaltered. Therefore the sum of all terms of the characteristic is the same as the sum of all the terms of the original row; in the case when the characteristic consists of one term only its value is just the value of that sum. As far as the case of a characteristic of two terms is concerned, we shall learn to calculate the values of its terms (without working out all intermediate derived rows) in the following section. And now we shall state the general question. When does the characteristic of a row consist of one, and when of two terms? First we shall attempt to clarify how things stand by means of a 'mathematical experiment'. For this purpose, we shall work out the characteristics of several rows of the type 1, 2, 3, ..., n. We shall write down the consecutive derived rows one underneath the other and we shall underline the middle terms:

<u>Example 1.</u>   α   1 <u>2</u> 3

          α'   4 2

<u>Example 2.</u>   α   1 <u>2</u> <u>3</u> 4

          α'   3 <u>4</u> 3

          α"   10

A PROBLEM IN THE THEORY OF NUMBERS (FORMULATION) 41

Example 3. α   1 2 <u>3</u> 4   5
          α'   2 <u>5   4</u> 4
          α''   7 <u>6</u>   2
          α'''   5 10

Example 4. α   1 2 <u>3   4</u> 5 6
          α'   2 4 <u>5</u>   5 5
          α''   4 <u>9   5</u> 3
          α'''   1 <u>12</u> 8
          α''''   14   7

Example 5. α   1 2 3 <u>4</u> 5 6 7
          α'   2 3 <u>6   5</u> 6 6
          α''   3 8 <u>7</u> 6 4
          α'''   8 <u>13   6</u> 1
          α''''   7 <u>14</u> 7
          α'''''   28

Example 6. α   1 2 3 <u>4   5</u> 6 7 8
          α'   2 3 5 <u>6</u>   6 7 7
          α''   3 5 <u>10   6</u> 7 5
          α'''   5 13 <u>9</u> 7 2
          α''''   3 <u>13 13</u> 7
          α'''''   16 <u>16</u> 4
          α''''''   12 24

42   SOME APPLICATIONS OF MECHANICS TO MATHEMATICS

Example 7.

α	1	2	3	4	<u>5</u>	6	7	8	9
α'		2	3	4	<u>7</u>	<u>6</u>	7	8	8
α''			3	4	9	<u>8</u>	7	8	6
α'''				4	9	<u>14</u>	<u>7</u>	8	3
α''''					1	9	<u>17</u>	10	8
α'''''						9	<u>19</u>	<u>10</u>	7
α''''''							2	<u>26</u>	17
α'''''''								30	15

The examples shown indicate, that the characteristic of a row representing a segment of the natural series can consist of one of two terms. In addition, we notice the following regularity: the characteristic consists of one term, if $n=3k+1$, otherwise it consists of two terms. At the same time a new and interesting peculiarity reveals itself: if the characteristic consists of two terms, then one is twice the other. Thus the following curious theorem takes shape.

<u>The characteristic of the row</u> 1, 2, 3, ..., n <u>consists of one term, when</u> $n=3k+1$. <u>It consists of two terms, when</u> $n=3k$ <u>or</u> $n=3k+2$. <u>In the latter case one of the two terms (the first one when</u> $n=3k$, <u>the second one when</u> $n=3k+2$, <u>is twice the other</u>.

This theorem will be proved in the next section; at the same time the general question will also not be forgotten. For what kind of rows does the characteristic consist of one, and for what kinds of rows of two terms?

10. A PROBLEM IN THE THEORY OF NUMBERS (SOLUTION)

We give our problem a new, mechanical, interpretation. Instead of a row of numbers $P_1, P_2, \ldots, P_n$ we shall consider a rod (Fig. 32a) loaded at points $A_1, A_2, \ldots, A_n$ (such that $A_1A_2 = A_2A_3 = \ldots = A_{n-1}A_n$) by means of weights $P_1, P_2, \ldots, P_n$. Then a new set of loads corresponds to a derived row.

Fig. 32

We shall show that the material centre of a derived system of loads coincides with the material centre of the original system.

Let us split up mentally each of the end loads P_1 and P_n into two point loads

$$P_1 = P + (P_1 - P), \quad P_n = P + (P_n - P),$$

where P is the smallest of the loads P_1 and P_n (so that at least one of the loads $P_1 - P$ and $P_n - P$ equals zero). Then the system of loads α can be represented as a union of two systems. System $\underline{\alpha}$ consisting of loads $P_1 - P, P_2, \ldots P_{n-1}, P_n - P$ (pictured underneath the rod in Fig. 32b), and the system $\bar{\alpha}$ consisting of two loads of weight P each (pictured above the rod in Fig. 32b). In the transition to the derived system of loads all loads of the system $\underline{\alpha}$ remain where they were, and the loads of the system $\bar{\alpha}$ come closer together, each moving the same distance (in order to be added to the middle terms). In other words, the derived system α is a combination of two systems α' and $\bar{\alpha}'$, of which the system α coincides with the system α and the system $\bar{\alpha}'$ is obtained from the system $\bar{\alpha}$ by means of bringing both loads of the latter an equal distance closer together. In as much as, obviously, $\bar{\alpha}'$ and $\bar{\alpha}$ are equivalent, then, from the proposition 3 of Section 5, systems α and α' are also equivalent, and material centres of equivalent systems coincide. Thus, in the transition from a system of loads to its derived one, the material centre (i.e. the centre of gravity) of the system does not change. Therefore, it does not change in the transition from the original system to its characteristic.

In this way, the characteristic is one or two point loads having the same centre of gravity as the initial system of loads. Note, also, that the positions of the point loads making up the characteristic coincide with the positions of some of the loads of the initial system, i.e. with certain of the points $A_1, \ldots, A_n$. If the characteristic contains two loads then these loads are situated in neighbouring points, A_j and A_{j+1}, and the centre of gravity of the characteristic is to be found between them. Therefore the characteristic consists of just one load only in the case, when its centre of gravity (or, which is the same, the centre of gravity of the original system) coincides with one of the points $A_1, \ldots, A_n$.

According to Section 8, the centre of gravity of the original system has as its abscissa

$$\frac{P_1 a_1 + P_2 a_2 + \ldots + P_n a_n}{P_1 + P_2 + \ldots + P_n},$$

where $a_1, \ldots, a_n$ are the abscissae of points $A_1, \ldots, A_n$. If we take $a_1 = 1, a_2 = 2, \ldots, a_n = n$, then the abscissa of the centre of gravity can be expressed by means of the formula

$$\frac{P_1 \cdot 1 + P_2 \cdot 2 + \ldots + P_n \cdot n}{P_1 + P_2 + \ldots + P_n}.$$

For the centre of gravity to coincide with one of the integral points $A_1, A_2, \ldots, A_n$ it is necessary and sufficient that its abscissa should be expressed as a whole number. Hence we have finally that <u>the characteristic of the row $P_1, P_2, \ldots, P_n$ consists of one term when and only when the number $\frac{P_1 \cdot 1 + P_2 \cdot 2 + \ldots + P_n \cdot n}{P_1 + P_2 + \ldots + P_n}$ is a whole number</u>.

A PROBLEM IN THE THEORY OF NUMBERS (SOLUTION)

In particular, if $P_1 = 1^2$, $P_2 = 2^2$, ..., $P_n = n^2$, then (see Example 3 in Section 8) the number $\dfrac{P_1 \cdot 1 + P_2 \cdot 2 + \ldots + P_n \cdot n}{P_1 + \ldots + P_n}$ equals $\dfrac{3n(n+1)}{2(2n+1)}$. This number is never a whole one (except in the trivial case of $n=1$). Indeed, if this number were whole then the number $4\dfrac{3n(n+1)}{2(2n+1)}$ would also be whole. Then the difference

$$4\frac{3n(n+1)}{2(2n+1)} - (3n+1) = \frac{n-1}{2n+1}.$$

would also be whole.

But the number $\dfrac{n-1}{2n+1}$ is a whole number only in the case $n-1=0$, thus, when $n > 1$ the characteristic of the row $1, 4, 9, \ldots, n^2$ always consists of two numbers.

If $P_1 = 1$, $P_2 = 2$, ..., $P_n = n$, then (see Example 1, Section 8) the number $\dfrac{2n+1}{3}$ is the value of the expression $\dfrac{P_1 \cdot 1 + \ldots + P_n \cdot n}{P_1 + \ldots + P_n}$. If $n = 3k+1$, then the number $\dfrac{2n+1}{3} = 2k+1$ is a whole number and the characteristic consists of one term. If $n = 3k$, then $\dfrac{2n+1}{3} = 2k + \dfrac{1}{3}$; if $n = 3k+2$, then $\dfrac{2n+1}{3} = (2k+1) + \dfrac{2}{3}$; in both latter cases $\dfrac{2n+1}{3}$ is not a whole number and the characteristic consists of two terms. Thus, the first part of the theorem, formulated at the end of the previous section, is proved.

If $n = 3k$, the centre of gravity of the system of loads $1, 2, \ldots, n$ has, as just shown, the abscissa $2k + \dfrac{1}{3}$ and is, therefore, situated between the points A_{2k} and A_{2k+1}. Therefore, the loads making up the characteristic of the initial system are situated at these very points. Since the centre of gravity turned out to be twice as near to point A_{2k} as to point A_{2k+1}, then, of the two loads of the characteristic, the one situated at A_{2k} is twice as large as the one situated at A_{2k+1}. Thus we get, that in the case where $n = 3k$, the first term of the characteristic is twice the second one. If now $n = 3k+2$, then the abscissa of the centre of gravity equals $(2k+1) + \dfrac{2}{3}$. The centre of gravity in this case is situated between the points A_{2k+1} and A_{2k+2}, and is twice as near to the second of these points as to the first. Therefore the load (of the characteristic) situated at the second point is twice as heavy as the load in the first point; in other words, the second term of the characteristic is twice the first one. Thus, the theorem of Section 9 is fully proved.

The sum of the terms of the characteristic of row 1, 2, ..., n equals the sum of the terms of the row itself, i.e. $1+2+\ldots+n=\frac{n(n+1)}{2}$ (see Example 1 in Section 8). Knowing that one of these terms is twice the other we can calculate the terms themselves. We obtain the following values for them: $\frac{n(n+1)}{6}$ (the smaller term) and $\frac{n(n+1)}{3}$ (the greater term).

Finally, the characteristic of the row 1, 2, ..., n has the following form

$$\frac{n(n+1)}{3}, \frac{n(n+1)}{6} \quad \text{(if } n=3k\text{)},$$

$$\frac{n(n+1)}{2} \quad \text{(if } n=3k+1\text{)},$$

$$\frac{n(n+1)}{6}, \frac{n(n+1)}{3} \quad \text{(if } n=3k+2\text{)}.$$

Generally, in order to calculate the characteristic of the row $P_1, P_2, \ldots, P_n$, we proceed as follows. Firstly, the number

$$x = \frac{P_1 \cdot 1 + P_2 \cdot 2 + \ldots + P_n \cdot n}{P_1 + P_2 + \ldots + P_n}.$$

is found.

If x is a whole number, the characteristic consists of one term whose value equals the sum $P_1 + P_2 + \ldots + P_n$. If x is not a whole number, it is necessary to rewrite x in the form

$$x = y + z,$$

where y is whole and $0 < z < 1$. In this case the characteristic consists of two numbers Q_1 and Q_2, while

$$Q_1 + Q_2 = P_1 + P_2 + \ldots + P_n \qquad (1)$$

Since Q_1 and Q_2 can be thought of as loads situated at points with abscissae y and $y+1$ and having a centre of gravity at the point with abscissa x, then (according to

Section 5)
$$\frac{Q_1}{Q_2} = \frac{1-z}{z}. \qquad (2)$$

Solving (1) and (2) simultaneously we find Q_1 and Q_2:

$$Q_1 = \frac{1-z}{z} Q_2, \quad \frac{1}{z} Q_2 = \frac{1-z}{z} Q_2 + Q_2 = Q_1 + Q_2 = P_1 + \ldots + P_n,$$
$$Q_2 = (P_1 + \ldots + P_n) z, \quad Q_1 = (P_1 + \ldots + P_n)(1-z). \qquad (3)$$

As an example of the latter case, let us find the characteristic of the row 1, 4, 9, ..., n^2 $(n>1)$. We saw before that in this case $x = \frac{3n(n+1)}{2(2n+1)}$ and the characteristic consists of two numbers. In order to calculate the terms of the characteristic, it is necessary to find z first. For this purpose we put $n = 4k + r$, where $r = 0, 1, 2, 3$. Then

$$x = \frac{3n(n+1)}{2(2n+1)} = \frac{3(4k+r)(4k+r+1)}{2[2(4k+r)+1]} = 3k + \frac{3}{2} \cdot \frac{2k + 4kr + r + r^2}{8k + 2r + 1}.$$

If $r=0$, then $x = 3k + \frac{3}{2} \cdot \frac{2k}{8k+1} = 3k + \frac{3k}{8k+1}$; therefore, $z = \frac{3k}{8k+1} = \frac{v}{2n+1}$, where $v = 3k$.

If $r=1$, then $x = 3k + \frac{3}{2} \cdot \frac{6k+2}{8k+3} = 3k + 1 + \frac{k}{8k+3}$, therefore, $z = \frac{k}{8k+3} = \frac{v}{2n+1}$, where $v = k$.

If $r=2$, then $x = 3k + \frac{3}{2} \cdot \frac{10k+6}{8k+5} = 3k + 1 + \frac{7k+4}{8k+5}$, therefore, $z = \frac{7k+4}{8k+5} = \frac{v}{2n+1}$, where $v = 7k+4$.

If $r=3$, then $x = 3k + \frac{3}{2} \cdot \frac{14k+12}{8k+7} = 3k + 2 + \frac{5k+4}{8k+7}$, therefore, $z = \frac{5k+4}{8k+7} = \frac{v}{2n+1}$, where $v = 5k+4$.

The sum of the terms of the characteristic equals $1^2 + 2^2 + \ldots + n^2 = \frac{n(n+1)(2n+1)}{6}$ (see Example 1 in Section 8). The terms of the characteristic are calculated according to formulae (3)

$$Q_2 = \frac{n(n+1)(2n+1)}{6} z = \frac{n(n+1)(2n+1)}{6} \frac{v}{2n+1} = \frac{n(n+1)v}{6},$$

$$Q_1 = \frac{n(n+1)(2n+1)}{6}(1-z) = \frac{n(n+1)(2n+1)}{6} \frac{2n+1-v}{2n+1} =$$

$$= \frac{n(n+1)(2n+1-v)}{6}.$$

Substituting here **4k, 4k+1, 4k+2, 4k+3** for **n** and taking into account the dependence of **v** on **k**, we finally get that the characteristic of row 1, 4, 9, ..., n^2 is of the form

$$\frac{2k(4k+1)(5k+1)}{3}, \quad 2k^2(4k+1) \qquad \text{(if } n=4k\text{),}$$

$$\frac{(2k+1)(4k+1)(7k+3)}{3}, \quad \frac{k(2k+1)(4k+1)}{3} \qquad \text{(if } n=4k+1\text{),}$$

$$\frac{(k+1)(2k+1)(4k+3)}{3}, \quad \frac{(2k+1)(4k+3)(7k+4)}{3} \qquad \text{(if } n=4k+2\text{),}$$

$$2(k+1)^2(4k+3), \quad \frac{2(k+1)(4k+3)(5k+4)}{3} \qquad \text{(if } n=4k+3\text{).}$$

11. THE IMPOSSIBILITY OF PERPETUAL MOTION

We now consider any convex polygon and a point O inside it. Let us draw perpendiculars from the point O to the sides of the polygon. The feet of the perpendiculars can be on the sides themselves (like, for instance, the perpendicular dropped on the side *AB* in Fig. 33) or on the sides produced (like the perpendiculars to the sides *FA* and *EF* in the same figure). It can happen, of course, that the feet of all the perpendiculars lie on the sides themselves. This

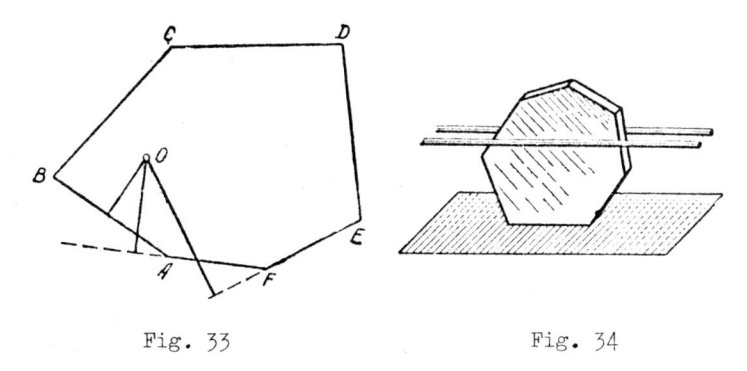

Fig. 33   Fig. 34

happens if O is the centre of a regular polygon). The question arises: can it happen that the feet of all the perpendiculars are not on the sides themselves, but on those sides produced? It turns out that this cannot happen, i.e. the foot of at least one perpendicular lies on the corresponding side (and not on its extension).

To prove this proposition we make use of the principle enunciated in the heading of this chapter. We picture our polygon in the shape of a thin lamina with the centre of gravity at the point O (we can, for instance, consider the lamina as weightless and that there is a point load at O). Let us stand the polygon on its edge on a horizontal table. If we sit it up strictly vertically, it will not fall; if desired, it can be regarded as supported on both sides by means of guide-rails (Fig. 34). The polygon will either remain standing or begin to roll; if it rolls it will have to come to a stop anyway (otherwise we would have perpetual motion. In the position in which it comes to rest the perpendicular from the centre of gravity must intersect the edge of support by Proposition 2 of Section 5). Thus we found the side of the polygon for which the foot of the perpendicular from O lies on it itself.

A similar theorem holds for a polyhedron. Namely, suppose we have a convex polyhedron and a point O inside it. Let us drop perpendiculars from the point O to all the plane faces of the polyhedron. Then the foot of at least one of these perpendiculars lies on the face itself (and not on its extension).

For proof, we picture the polyhedron as a solid body with its centre of gravity at O. (We can, for instance, regard the polyhedron as being weightless and place a point load at O.) We now stand our polyhedron on any of its faces on a horizontal floor. The polyhedron will either remain in equilibrium, or it will roll; in the latter case it will sooner or later come to rest in a position of equilibrium. Thus there exists a position in which the polyhedron stands on the floor motionless. Let us consider the face which is its plane of support. On the grounds of proposition 2, Section 5, the perpendicular drawn from O to the plane of that face passes through that face itself. Thus, we found a face satisfying the demands stated in the theorem.

CONCLUSION

All the problems which we have examined could be solved by purely mathematical means. It should not be thought, however, that the utilization of mechanical considerations in solving mathematical problems is only a game. Such methods have a historical and a practical significance.

Archimedes used the laws of equilibrium to find the areas of curved figures: thus, in order to find the area of a parabolic segment (i.e. a figure bounded by an arc of a parabola and the chord joining its ends), he 'suspended' the segment at the end of a lever. At all times mechanical and physical considerations have exercised and still exercise a substantial influence on the derivation of mathematical results (if not in the form of a direct proof then as helpful reasoning).

The application of the laws of mechanics to mathematics is just a particular case of a general method consisting of making inverse use of the connexion between natural phenomena and their mathematical description. To describe any phenomenon mathematically means to find formulae enabling us to calculate the physical characteristics of this phenomenon (speeds, temperatures, distances and so on) or to find equations whose solutions are the characteristics indicated.

The direct ultilization of a mathematical description consists of the fact that we can discover the numerical values of those characteristics, without observing the phenomenon itself, but by carrying out calculations according to appropriate formulae, or by solving appropriate equations. It is useful to act in this way when the phenomenon itself is complicated and its mathematical description is simple.

It is, however, possible to proceed in another way: instead of working out the values of formulae or solving equations, we can realize the phenomenon itself by means of an experiment, measure the characteristics that interest us and thus obtain the values occurring in formulae and the solutions of equations experimentally.

Such a procedure is useful when we deal with complicated formulae and difficult equations, which describe, however, phenomena which are easily reproduced in the laboratory. This principle lies at the basis of modelling (i.e. investigating physical processes using models) for which the following procedure is followed. It is required to investigate the process A (modelled); this process is describable by the formulae and equations E; at the same time E serves as the description of the process A' (the modelling process) realizable in laboratory conditions; the process A' is realized; in this way the values of formulae and the solutions of equations E are found and therefore the required properties of the process A are established. It is said about the process A (and also about the formulae and equations E), that it is modelled by the process A. Let us also add that if, two processes are described by the same formulae and equations, then one speaks of analogy existing between them. The simplest instance of modelling is the solution of the Steinhaus problem presented in Section 4. The modelled phenomenon A is the walking to school by the children; the characteristic of interest to us is the time taken. This time is the value of a certain formula. The modelling phenomenon A' is found (the suspending of leads on threads) where the value of the formula is the amount of potential energy. The latter phenomenon is realized experimentally.

The method of modelling has a great practical significance. (Electrical and hydraulic phenomena are chiefly used to provide models.) In particular, this method lies at the basis of many types of so called 'integrating machines'; we shall now acquaint ourselves with the principle of action of the simplest of them - the frictional integrator.

Suppose we have a straight line p, and a curve l lying on one side of this straight line (Fig. 35), while any perpendicular to p intersects l in not more than one point. Let us take two such perpendiculars, AB and CD, and we shall try to find the area S of the curved trapezium $ABDC$. For this, let us divide the segment AC into tiny parts by means of points

$$X_1 = A, \; X_2, \; X_3, \; \ldots, \; X_n, \; X_{n+1} = C$$

(in Fig. 36, $n = 6$). In each of the segments $X_i X_{i+1}$ we pick a point T_i, at which we raise a perpendicular to intersect the curve l at the point Y_i. At each point Y_i we draw straight lines parallel to p to meet the perpendiculars from points X_i. The area S of the stairlike figure shaded-in in Fig. 36 is approximately equal to the area S of the curved trapezium, and it becomes closer to the latter, the smaller are the segments $X_i X_{i+1}$ into which the base AC is divided.

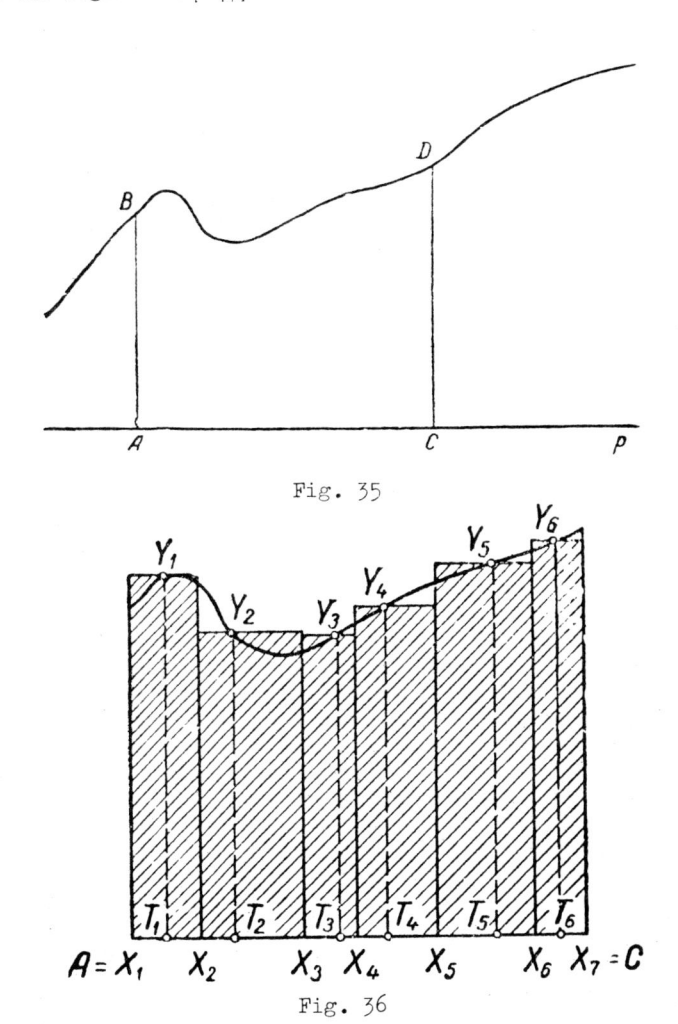

Fig. 35

Fig. 36

54 SOME APPLICATIONS OF MECHANICS TO MATHEMATICS

Let the lengths of segments $X_1, X_2, \ldots, X_n X_{n+1}$ equal respectively $\alpha_1, \ldots, \alpha_n$ and the lengths of segments $T_1 Y_1, \ldots, T_n Y_n$ equal respectively $y_1, \ldots, y_n$. Then area S' equals

$$\alpha_1 y_1 + \cdots + \alpha_n y_n. \tag{1}$$

We now consider a system consisting of a disk I and a wheel II pressed at its rim to the disk I (Fig. 37). The wheel II can move along its axis. At a certain instant, let the distance of the wheel II from the centre O of the disk I equal y.

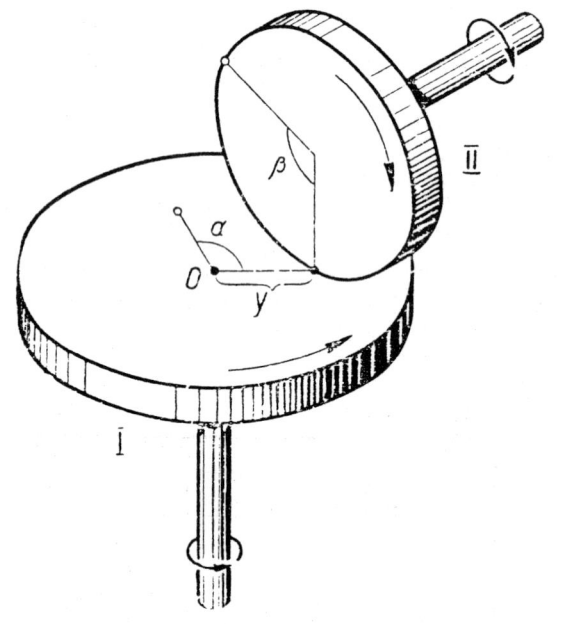

Fig. 37

Suppose that we rotate the disk I through an angle α (in radian measure). The point of the disk which had touched the wheel II before rotating will have described an arc equal to αy. The same distance is traversed by a point on the rim of the wheel II. The wheel II rotates through an angle β in the process. Since a point on the circumference of the wheel traverses an arc βr while the wheel rotates through the angle β, where r = radius of wheel II, then $\alpha y = \beta r$. Let us take $r = 1$; then $\beta = \alpha y$. If we now place the wheel II

CONCLUSION

at a distance y_1 from the centre O and turn the disk by α_1, then place the wheel II at a distance y_2 from the centre O and turn the disk by an angle α_2 and so on, finally place the wheel II at a distance y_n from centre O and turn the disk by an angle α_n, then the total angle through which the wheel II rotates as a result of these operations will equal numerically the quantity (1), i.e. the area S' of the stairlike figure shaded in in Fig. 36.

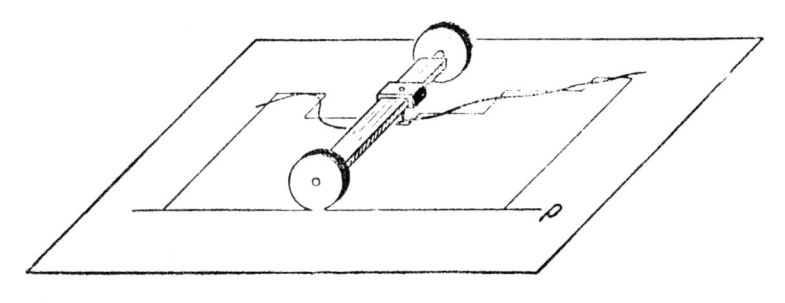

Fig. 38

Let us draw a straight line p and a curve l on a sheet of paper (Fig. 38) and consider the following mechanism: a track is attached to two little wheels, one of which rolls along the straight line p (in such a way that the track is always perpendicular to this straight line). A slide can move along the track. In the middle of the slide there is a stylo, whose end touches the paper. Let us imagine, that the track is connected to the disk I and the wheel II in the following manner: the rotation of the wheel of the track causes the disk to rotate through the same angle; the distance of the wheel II from the centre O of the disk I is, at any instant, equal to the distance of the middle of the slide from the beginning of the track. The radius of the little wheel of the track is taken to equal 1. We proceed to trace the contour of the stairlike figure with the stylo. While we are doing this, the track rolls along the straight line p and the slide moves along the track. From what was said in the previous paragraph it follows that, as a result, the wheel II will rotate by an amount equal to the area S'. The finer the division into parts of segment AC, the closer is the broken line making up the contour of the stairlike figure to the curve l, and the closer S' approximates S. If, therefore, we trace the curve itself, instead of the broken line, with the stylo, then the wheel II will rotate by an amount equal to S. The rotation of the wheel II can be registered on a special scale.

The modelled process in this case is the process of measuring the area of the curved trapezium by means of calculating the areas of stairlike figures. This process is described by means of formula (1). It turns out that the same formula describes a certain other process, connected with the frictional mechanism depicted in Fig. 37. This allows us to model the formula (1) and the process of measuring areas expressed by it, by means of the mechanism shown.

Thus, mechanical analogies have lead us to an instrument for the calculation of areas of curved figures (at least, figures of a special type - curved trapeziums*).

In ending this account we make one remark of a general character. All the reasoning based on the introduction of mechanical considerations can appear incorrect to fussy readers. Even the first and simplest example discussed in Section 1 is capable of producing objections. Indeed, the thread is not a straight line (it has thickness and if it is seen through a microscope it appears quite irregular in form) so that the phrase 'the thread is stretched along a straight line' has no exact sense. Further we cannot, strictly speaking, talk about the end of the thread as a point (and even the very statement that the load is attached to the thread at a definite point is also not without flaw). Finally any real material thread is extensible, therefore the length of the thread with the load is greater than the length of the thread alone.

It would be possible to put forward many critical remarks of this kind, relating both to the above reasoning and to similar arguments which lie at the basis of all our subject matter. We should not, however, think that these criticisms rob this reasoning of its value in finding out the truth. We consider it no less convincing than geometrical proofs. The crux of the matter is contained in the fact that all our propositions about threads, loads, etc. are approximate only, and are fulfilled the more exactly the more perfect are the properties of the object used by us (thread, load, etc.). In our case certain statements (e.g. 'the thread is stretched

---

*Instruments, which give the area of a curved trapezium by means of tracing its curved side are called <u>integrometers</u>. Instruments giving the area of any figure by means of tracing its complete outline are called planimeters.

CONCLUSION

along a straight line') are fulfilled the more exactly the thinner the thread chosen. In such a case it is said that the statement is fulfilled for an infinitely thin thread. Other statements (e.g. that the length of the thread with the lead and the length of the thread without the load are equal) are the more nearly satisfied the less extensible is the thread; in such a case it is said that these statements are fulfilled for an absolutely inextensible thread. It is clear that there do not exist in nature any infinitely thin or absolutely inextensible threads. It is just as ideal a concept as, for instance, the concept of the point of application of a force, well known from a school course; conclusions arrived at for forces applied at points are more exactly satisfied the smaller the area of interaction of forces. The concept of material points is just such an idealization. The facts established for material points are more nearly satisfied for real bodies the smaller their dimensions are.

We should like to emphasize here, that all the concepts and laws of mechanics (as of physics in general) are connected with the idealization of natural phenomena, therefore even a schoolboy, without perhaps being aware of it, comes across such idealizations at every step. Let us take, for example, one of the elementary concepts of mechanics - the concept of uniform motion. There does not exist in nature any completely uniform motion (careful measurements reveal that even clock hands move irregularly). In many cases, however, the irregularity is so small that it can be profitably ignored. Thus there arises the idea of uniform motion. The same can be said about Newton's first law of motion: in fact, no bodies exist which are not acted upon by other bodies. One could continue a list of similar examples indefinitely: they permeate all physics.

Thus, we see that mechanics operates, fundamentally, not with real but with ideal bodies and with processes such as 'a body, not acted upon by other bodies', 'rectilinear uniform motion' etc. But we handle these ideal objects as if they were real ones, i.e. as if they existed in actual life.

Note, finally, that mechanical abstractions (such as a material point, weightless, infinitely thin, absolutely inextensible thread, and others) are not in the slightest degree different in their nature from geometrical abstractions (such as a point, a straight line, a plane, and so on).

In fact, points, straight lines, and planes do not exist in nature in the form of real objects and the real sense of the propositions made about them is, that they are fulfilled the more exactly, the closer the properties of the given real objects are to points, straight line, planes and so on.